Gates and Sti

by
Michael Roberts

Edited by Sara Roadnight

Photographs by David Hasted,
Roy Blake and others

Illustrations by Sara Roadnight

This book is dedicated to all those farmers who lost their livestock and their living as a result of the epidemic of Foot and Mouth Disease in 2001.

Published by Gold Cockerel Books
ISBN 0947870 32 6

Printed by Bartlett Printing
Swan Yard, Okehampton Street, St Thomas, Exeter, Devon
Tel. 01392 254086

Conditions of Sale

ERRATA

Page 59   Ribchester, Lancs instead of Plumpton, Yorks.
Page 76   Higham Hall, Dubwath instead of Bigham Hall, Durwath.
Page 91   This stile is at Gayle with Hawes church in view.
Page 97   Hillfoot Farm instead of Willfoot Farm.
Page 120   Cocklick Hill instead of Cockwill Hill.
Page 121   Higher Barrowford instead of Higher Barronford.

Our apologies for this.

Concerning....

All acts of initiative and creation, there is one elementary truth, the ignorance of which kills countless ideas and splendid plans. The moment one definitely commits oneself, then Providence moves too. All manner of things occur to help one that would never otherwise have occurred, a whole stream of events issue from the decision, raising in one's favour all manner of unforeseen incidents and meetings and material assistance which no man could have dreamed would come. Whatever you do, or dream you can do, begin it. All this has genius, power and magic in it. Begin it now.

GOETHE

INTRODUCTION

I have tried to bring together as many different types of farm gates and stiles as possible. With David Hasted's help, the stiles have for the first time been classified into different categories: overs, throughs, combinations and mechanical. As you will see, this is a large and diverse subject, and I hope I haven't offended anyone by leaving out their particular favourites, but I am always interested to hear from people who know of interesting or unusual stiles or farm gates.

An OS box has been provided for those of you who might care to fill them in when you have found the stiles illustrated in this book. They are either on recognised footpaths or in churchyards, although I haven't seen them all. I only wish that more care was taken to preserve these old land-marks in our countryside.

I hope you enjoy reading this book as much as we have enjoyed putting it together and being in contact with all the kind people who have contributed to it.

Michael Roberts and Sara Roadnight
Kennerleigh, Devon
May 2001

Contents   page

Acknowledgements

This book would not have been possible without the generous time and assistance given by the following people or organisations:

Catherine Aneja

Margaret Bailey

Roy Blake

Beamish Museum

Derrick Beavis

Major Richard Bower

Cambridge & County Folk Museum

Centrewire

Chris Cole

Corinium Museum

D G Cornford

Mrs J Bryne Daniel

East Sussex County Council (Archives Department)

Dick Elliot of Farnells Ltd.

Pam & Doug Ellis

Nyree Fearnley

Jenny Filby

Rosalind Hallet

Robin Hammond

David Hasted

Horsham Museum

John A Hudson

Susan Jones

Dorothy Kyne

Hazel Massey

Museum of East Anglia Life

Museum of Lincolnshire Life

Museum of Rural Life, Reading

Museum of Welsh Life

Ron & Liz Norton

Ryedale Folk Museum

Somerset Rural Life Museum

Mary Slater

Peter Spencer

Greg Taylor

Rose Whicheloe

Barbara Woodyatt

The Zennor Museum

The History of Gates

The history of gates goes hand in hand with enclosures. There are traces of very ancient fields in many parts of England, cleared of scrub and woodland, mainly on chalk and limestone soils, but fields made by the Celts during the Bronze Age (about 800 - 700 BC) through to the Iron age, are still to be found today in Pembrokeshire and Cornwall near Zennor, west of St. Ives. These fields range in size from 1/3 of an acre to about three acres, and were cleared of most of their stones which were piled up round the edges to make walls which gave shelter to livestock. In early times man settled in different areas and cleared trees, scrub and stones to make room for his animals to graze. He made crude gates with poles or hurdles to prevent his livestock from wandering and to protect them at night, when they were brought into the settlement or stockade to keep them safe from wolves, bears and wild boar. As the ancient Britons improved their farming methods, so more enclosures were made to protect new emerging crops from domestic and wild animals. The forests were all important as a source of food and essential materials such as deer and wild boar meat, (later the prerogative of kings and noblemen), nuts such as beech, hazel, chestnuts and acorns which were used for eating or fed to pigs, branches for cattle fodder fed green or dried, wood and charcoal. As predators were brought under control, sheep, goats and cows could be safely left outside at night, either tethered or in gated enclosures. The early gates were hurdles made of hazel or willow.

When the Romans arrived in AD 43, there was a thriving but primitive agricultural system, which was even exporting grain to France. The Romans with their experience of empire set about modernising the farming system by draining the fields and planting hedges in order to be able to feed their armies. They brought with them several useful agricultural introductions such as improved breeds of sheep, pigs and chickens, ploughs, and swinging or hinged gates, to name but a few. Roman gates were similar to the gates and doors found in the Middle East today, which use a pole as a hinge. Their design was more sophisticated however as they fixed ferules or metal pivots at the top and bottom to provide a swinging closure with ease of opening which normally would have been used in

continued on page 7

1

Some of the oldest fields still being farmed today. These celtic fields near Zennor in north Cornwall are only a few acres in size. Note how big the farm-house seems to be in comparison and how large the black and white Friesians look in these fields. (M.D.L.R.) Celtic livestock, sheep and cows, were similar to Soay sheep and Dexter cattle and so were small in comparison with the commercial livestock of today.

In the more remote parts of the British Isles where timber was scarce, fields or enclosures were made by clearing areas of stones which were piled up round the edges to create walls; more stones were then heaped into the gaps which served as gateways. Examples of this can still be seen in north Cornwall and on the Aran islands off the west coast of Ireland. (M.D.L.R.)

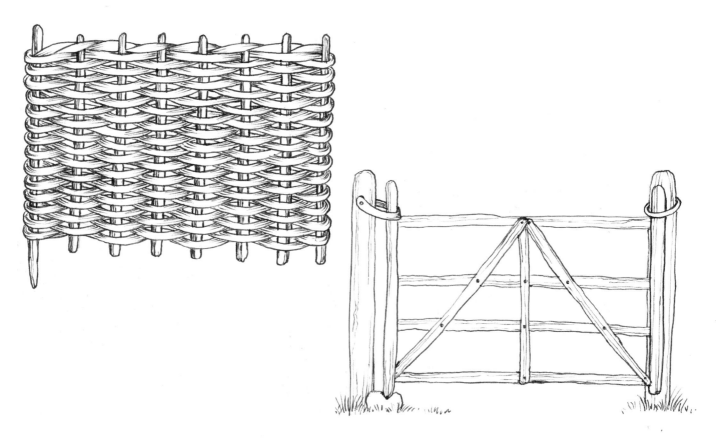

Two simple early gates. The wicker hurdle would have been used not only as a gate but also for fencing. Later a wooden hurdle, probably similar to the one illustrated, would have been used, complete with hinge and mellior stone. The hinge would have been either a leather strap or hazel pleaching, and the mellior stone had a shallow hole cut in it for the hinge post to pivot in.

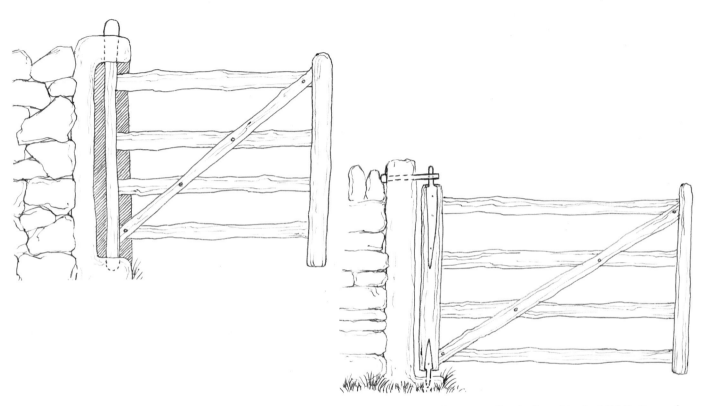

Left: the Romans introduced the first swinging gates into this country, and the same design is still to be found in the Middle East today, mainly on barns and granaries. The hinge post of the gate was pushed upwards through a hole in the stone gate post and then dropped into a hole at the bottom. Sometimes a metal ferrule was used on the bottom end of the hinge post. The illustration shows the type of gate that was probably used in earliest times. Right: later gate furniture or fittings evolved made in iron and a pivoting gate was made. The heel or hinge post was probably made of sawn timber, while the rest was made of cleft.

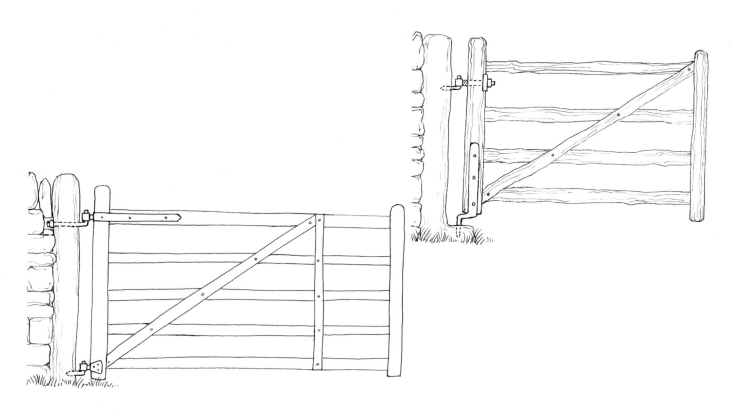

Right: gate furniture moved on to a simple adjustable top hinge bolt and eye. A large washer or plate on the inside would help to support this assembly. The bottom hinge may have been a pivot type.

Left: gate furniture as we know it today. The top band hinge covers the mortice joint to strengthen it, and the bottom band hinge is a simple affair. The forces of a gate work like this: the top of the gate is pulling away from the post, and the bottom of the gate at the hinge is being forced back against the post. The top hinge is now adjustable on the hook instead of the hinge.

conjunction with stone pillars. The idea caught on in the countryside, and was taken up by the local population, although to begin with they did not use metal parts. Gates made from woven hurdles very gradually gave way to hurdles made of cleft or split timber such as chestnut or ash. These would have been similar to the modern day sheep hurdle. The uprights would have been pointed at the bottom and morticed, using either a hot iron or auger and chisel, for the cross rails to slide into. The width of these hurdles/gates was probably 4ft - 6ft (1.30-1.90m). The Anglo-Saxons used the word 'geat' for gate, which can still be heard in the rural language of the south Midlands, and 'hlid geat' for swinging gate.

After 1066 the countryside was dominated by the Normans and the Monasteries. Enclosures gradually spread, especially in the north and the west, although strip farming would still be common for a long time to come. Enclosures were the result of several developments that took place over the next six centuries: the price of wool rose as sheep farming expanded thanks to the careful breeding of selected strains brought in by the Romans, Normans and Danes; the dissolution of the monasteries came about and their land was bought up by those enjoying the new found wealth of the New World; the Tudors began to import much larger cattle, and then a certain 'gentrification' of the countryside began to spread, funded by the wealth generated from the Industrial Revolution; and finally of course, political expediency became an important factor in the equation.

Celia Fiennes, writing towards the end of the 1600s, mentioned: "I entered in Devonshire 5 miles off from Wellington just on a high ridge of hills which discovers a vast prospect on each side full of inclosures". So in some parts of England a landscape of enclosed fields was still a novelty even in those days.

Before enclosures or fields most farming was open-plan, with strips of land being offered on a feudal basis to grow certain crops, and rights to cut hay on meadow land, with grazing rights on common land. Hedging spread gradually but it was not until the reign of George III (1760- 1820) that commissioners were appointed and hedge planting became a major feature of the time. It was at this point that the landscape of central, eastern and southern England was mainly shaped.

So the simple hurdle gate gave way to stronger and more elaborate swinging gates to cope with deer and the larger cattle introduced by the Tudors.

The pole gate appeared towards the start of the eighteenth century and was common in areas of rocky ground in the west and north of England. The posts or stoops were made of a solid piece of stone, roughly dressed and with holes or slots chiselled into them, one post with blind holes and the other post with stepped rectangular or round holes. Cross bars or rails would be put into the blind holes and then inserted into the stepped holes and pushed down. There are variants of this type of gatepost, some with holes through the posts, so that the cross rail can be slid in. Some of these posts bear inscriptions on them, initials and dates.

The width of these gateways was anything between 5ft and 9ft, but most were made for vehicular traffic as well as livestock. I am told by local people that these stone posts were so well dug into the ground that if you caught the hub of your cartwheel on one of them the wheel would be wrenched off. Another little anecdote concerned a farmer from Zeal Monachorum in Devon who traded cider for granite gateposts. These were cut on Dartmoor and delivered by cart in exchange for cider. The carthorse probably knew its way home quite well!

In the West of England and on the island of Aran in Ireland, the gaps leading into fields were filled with stones in the absence of trees with which to make gates, while in the south and east of England the Heaver or Heave gate was used to close entrances. This gate had no hinges and was dragged across the opening and hung on pegs or hooks on the fence posts either side. It would have been made of cleft or split local timber, and was rather a rough looking affair, probably made of different woods to keep the weight down, for instance, the posts could have been of oak, the rails of ash and the palings of chestnut or willow. It is still used with wire netting on by the Forestry Commission to keep rabbits out of new plantations.

continued on page 14

Early stockades for livestock in woodland areas would have been built of cleft or split wood and stakes driven into the ground. The poles were slid out to allow for the passage of the animals. This form of fencing was used by the early settlers on the eastern side of North America. The photograph was taken at the Museum of Welsh Life, St. Fagans near Cardiff. (M.D.L.R.)

NO ENTRY

Both these gates were photographed at Charlecote Park in Warwickshire, with typical cleft oak fencing similar to that found on several Midlands estates. This gate was to keep fallow deer and sheep in the park, but it has been 'doctored' in modern times. This type of fencing has been used for hundreds of years and probably originated in the seventeenth century. (M.D.L.R.)

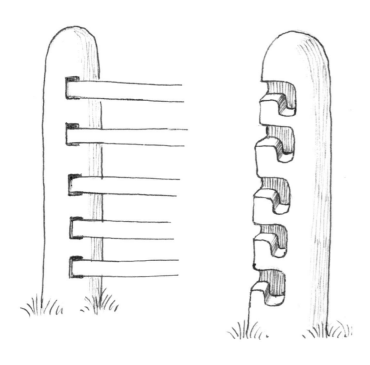

Pole gates appeared mainly on the western side of England, from Cumberland down to the West Country. Some of them had holes going through the stone posts, others had slots cut in the posts. (Beamish Museum)

11

Examples of pole gate posts to be found at North Bovey on Dartmoor in Devon. Note the interesting top hinge of the post on the right hand side. (M.D.L.R.)

This is a Dorset rod gate, mainly used for estate entrances, vicarages, etc., but very interesting because of the hinge system. Originally this would have been a metal onto wood hinge, but nowadays a brass ferrule is used inside the wooden hinge. Note the domed head gate post with a single throat. Winterbourne Zelston (M.D.L.R.)

As the Industrial Revolution developed, so the price of iron came down. Consequently it was used more and more in the countryside, and different forms of hinges, gate hooks and fastenings appeared. By 1850 standard gate furniture was being produced industrially and probably more cheaply than local blacksmiths could manage.

At this point, with an increasing demand on agriculture to feed the growing urban population, swinging gates with metal hinges were becoming more popular, and of course easier to use. So the hurdle and the 'Heaver' gate became more refined with sawn heels and heads, and later machinery became available to mortice holes for the rails. Heels were made of sawn timber so that the standardised hinges or bands would slide over and fit.

Another variation was the wooden sliding pole gate. A gap was made in traditional cleft rail fencing, and two posts were placed side by side to allow two or three rails to be inserted, forming a barrier. This type of gate transferred across to North America where there was an abundance of wood from the clearing of the forests. A few examples of these could also still be found in this country after the Second World War, mainly I think because of the shortage of proper gates. The rail holders were often made of old horseshoes, sharpened and banged into wooden posts, but there were also large square and round staples purpose made for the job.

And so evolved the modern farm gate as we know it today.

Two different centre pivoting Tapsel gates. These are nearly always used in churchyards as they allowed pall bearers to pass either side with the coffin in the middle. The left hand photograph was taken at Coombes, Lancing near Brighton, and the right hand one at Pyecombe just off the A23 north of Brighton. (M.D.L.R. & Roy Blake.)

Tapsel Gates

According to William J Roberts, writing in the Sussex County magazine in the 1940s: " Tapsel gates are essentially Sussex, for I know of nothing similar in other counties". (There are in fact, other examples of centre pivoting gates in Buckinghamshire, Middlesex, Gloucestershire, Devon, Hampshire and possibly more besides.)

"Only six examples are now to be seen, but doubtless there were many more in use when they were introduced as an ingenious and cheap method of preventing cattle from entering churchyards. This gate sought to displace the five barred gates in common use. It was constructed of light wood with slender stiles and bars. The only substantial detail in its make-up being the central pin or pivot upon which the nicely balanced gate is made to turn with the lightest touch. The pivot, made of oak or other hard wood, at times reinforced with metal, is firmly fixed in the ground and pierces the centre of the crossbars, through holes made for the purpose. The confines of the gate are so arranged that even when it is swung full circle, it must come to rest at the fixed stops on either side, to which it can be secured by hooks or by spring catches such as are shown in the Friston and East Dean gates."

"The design is particularly useful when only opened halfway, as it presents no obstacle to the bearers of a corpse, who may pass on either side without breaking step or shifting the burden."

"These gates are to be found at Coombes near Lancing, Pyecombe near Brighton, Kingston by Lewes, Friston, East Dean and Jevington."

"The name Tapsel is one to conjure with in Sussex and like many other surnames or place names, has many variants in spelling thus the name is sometimes spelt, Tapsel, Tapsell, Tapsil, Tapsayle, Tapsaille, Topsel and Topsil."

"The first recorded mention of the family, is to be found in the church warden's accounts of the parish of West Tarring where, under the date 1577 is the entry-Imprimis paid to Topsayle for casting of the bels (sic) the first payment iiis – (3 shillings.)"

"Thereafter and for many years, there are many entries relating to repartition of bells and ropes and for refreshment of labourers. All are concerned with the Tapsells, father and son, who were among the most noted of Sussex bell founders"

" Their home and foundry were in Church Lane, Tarring. Having thus established the antiquity of the family, I regret to state that, despite much effort I have not been able to fix a date when and by whom the Tapsel gate was invented. It was in all probability, one John Tapsel, a carpenter who lived near Mountfield in East Sussex, and who was married on 10th June 1753 at the Church of St Alfege, Greenwich to Sarah Hammond of that village."

One of the curious facts about the Tapsel gate, is that the design travelled to America.

These two lych gates are centre pivoting and have self-closing mechanisms.   (Lych comes from the Anglo-Saxon word 'lic' meaning a body).   As the gate is swung open, so the chain with the ball is wound up; it then closes with a clatter as the weight chain returns to its resting place.   On the left is the lych gate at Weston Turville, Buckinghamshire, and on the right the lych gate tucked away behind the shops at Chalfont St. Giles in Buckinghamshire. (M.D.L.R.)

People used to think that centre pivoting gates were only found in Sussex but they do occur in various other parts of the country, and were illustrated in estate catalogues during the nineteenth century. These two are interesting as they each have provision for a coffin to be supported on the top. This allowed for the bearers to catch their breath as they may have carried the body some way. It also enabled the first part of the burial service to be said under cover. If the dead person had died of an infectious disease, the burial service would have been held under the lych gate and at the graveside rather than in the church. In Cromwellian times no burial services were allowed. On the left is the gate at Duntisbourne Abbotts, Gloucestershire, and on the right the gate at Down St. Mary in Devon. Alfie Howard from Morchard Road has recently restored the Down St. Mary gate. (M.D.L.R.)

Patterns of Gate

It is not always possible to say that a certain pattern of gate is peculiar to a particular region or county. All we have been able to do is state where certain designs were made or found or mentioned in old books.

Gates were originally made by the village or estate carpenter, and the pattern was handed down from father to son and improved on over the years. Sometimes the estate owner dictated a pattern. As travel became easier in the 1700s with turnpikes and toll roads and later the railways, so a pattern of gate from one area would spread into another. The picture was further complicated by the advent of estate catalogues (about 1850) listing everything from gates to fountains, and as well as this, a farmer would sometimes move from one part of the country to another, taking his gates with him.

We have gone back as far as we can and you only have to look at the Devon gates for example, to see the variety of patterns that arose over the years. This could happen for many reasons: the estate owner or farmer wanted to be different from his neighbour, or the local carpenter wanted to use his own design for reasons of strength or economy, or a son was improving on his father's design as mentioned above; so some older gates can be rather a conundrum, although nowadays they are often made to a standard specification with diamond braces. As you drive along the country lanes, don't be surprised by the many variations you see along the way.

There follows a selection of photographs of gates showing the different patterns and variations that arise. You will probably find, once you have read this book, that as you drive along the country lanes in future, you will see the gates you pass with entirely new eyes!

Here are three gates with similar diagonal bars but different rails.

Left. This six barred gate is keeping livestock out of the churchyard at Old Burghclere in Hampshire. (Chris Cole)

Top. A five barred gate from Dorsington in Warwickshire, with a wooden catch and uprights rising above the top rail.

Bottom right. A very typical North Country sheep gate at the Beamish Museum in Tyne and Wear. (M.D.L.R.)

Top) A simple six barred seven foot gate constructed to keep lambs in. Note the fine blacksmith-made top hinge under the blackbird. Museum of Welsh Life, St. Fagans, Cardiff. (M.D.L.R.) Bottom) A typical estate or railway six barred gate, probably twelve feet long. Museum of Welsh Life, St. Fagans, Cardiff. (M.D.L.R.)

Long gates: Top) near Wintringham in Yorkshire; note the diagonals supporting the tapering top rail. (M.D.L.R.)

Bottom) a gate in Lincolnshire; there is a long diagonal from the bottom of the hinge post right through to the top of the head post and the uprights are dovetailed into the top rail. (Lincolnshire County Council)

Two variations of the same pattern gate: top) from Malton, Yorkshire, and bottom) from Umberleigh in Devon on a Forestry Commission plantation. This form of gate was made from lengths of 4" x 1" bolted together. Very much a budget gate. (M.D.L.R.)

Two delightful diamond gates from Malton in North Yorkshire. Notice the differences between the two designs. (M.D.L.R.)

Two gates of similar pattern. The left hand one of the pair of gates by the Thames at Day's Lock, Oxford (top) is very like the gate at Glastonbury Tor, (bottom) except that the latter also has diamond braces. Note the different tops of the gates and gateposts. (Chris Cole) & (M.D.L.R.)

These are common diamond braced gates, all with slight differences: top left) at Mary Arden's House, Wilmcote near Stratford on Avon, with spikes to stop trespassers; note also the nice wooden latch; top right) a ten foot gate from Pennymoor with the extra half uprights, and bottom) also from Pennymoor, an extension above the gate to keep the horses in. (M.D.L.R.)

These are two gates from North Cornwall made of timber although most of the old gates in Western Cornwall are mainly iron. This double top brace is unique to the area. (M.D.L.R.)

The next six photographs are mainly Devon gates with the single top brace, but look at the variations:

Top) A Devon gate at Kennerleigh.

Bottom left) I found this gate in Cornwall near Pendeen, but it is clearly a variation of a Devon gate.

Bottom right) A Devon gate extended to twelve feet at North Bovey. (M.D.L.R.)

Top left)   A Devon gate with a half upright in the middle at Morchard Bishop.
Bottom left)   A Devon gate with two half uprights in the middle.
Bottom right)   A bastard Devon gate made with diamond braces. (M.D.L.R.)

Top)   This is one of Richard Bower's estate gates, not strictly a farm gate but beautiful to behold. The heavy metal hinges hold it square. Winterbourne Zelston. (M.D.L.R.)

Bottom)   A pedestrian gate on the Two Moors Way with an interesting self-closing mechanism.   (Greg Taylor)

In some parts of England wrought iron gates were used in preference to wooden ones, particularly in parts of Yorkshire, Cornwall and Ireland. Whether this was to do with high rainfall, the salt spray in the air, the fashion at the time or the lack of suitable timber, we are not sure. The wooden gate at the bottom is an economy gate, sandwich-made with pieces of 4"x1". (M.D.L.R.)

Early gates were made of cleft branch wood rather than trunk wood, hence the origin of curved heel gates. (Trunk wood was used for building houses, barns or ships). These gates, (top left) are as near as you will find to the type and design which started to appear in Tudor times. The New Forest, Hampshire. (Richard Bower)

The posts for the gate would be morticed and the rails cut down to fit the mortise holes and banged on tight with the back of an axe head. The hinges would have been simple affairs as iron was expensive. To stop the gate sagging the diagonals would have been nailed to the rails with clout nails and flattened on the other side of the gate. The fastener would have been made of wood. This gate, bottom right is a modern equivalent. (M.D.L.R.)

Patterns of gates from around the country. Northern England

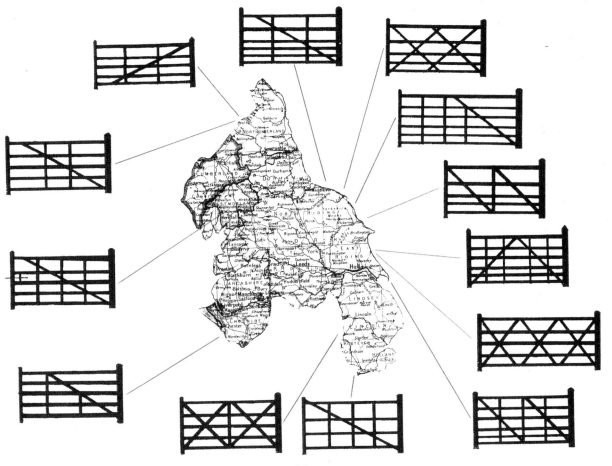

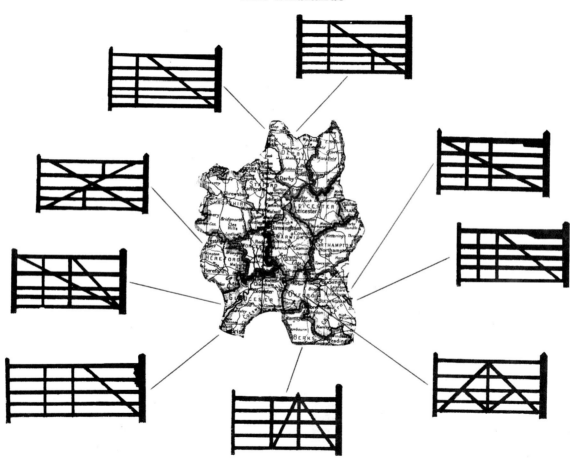

Wales

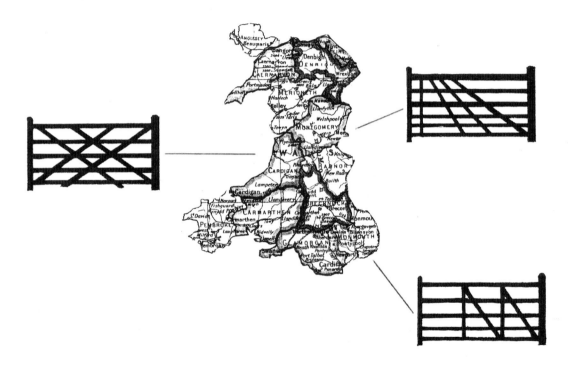

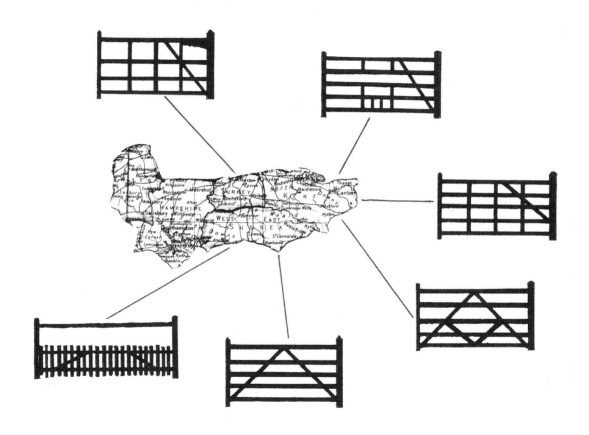

East Anglia

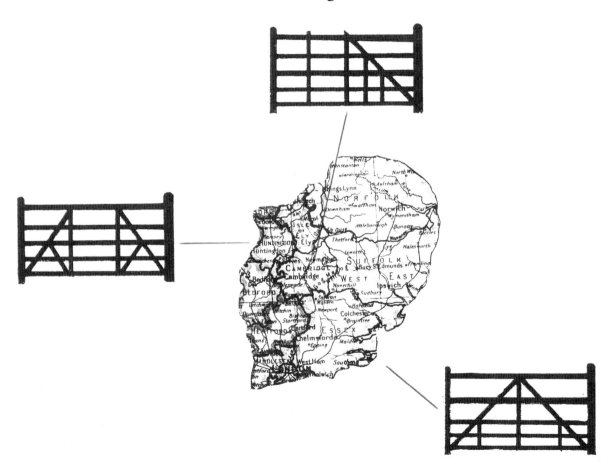

The South West

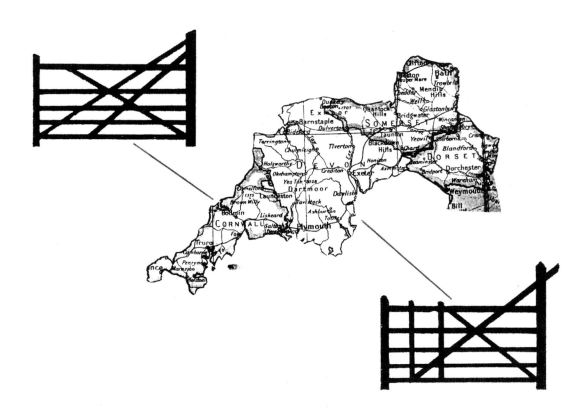

Names of gate parts:

3)
Back
Beam (Sussex)
Toprail
Top bar

6)
Downright
Jack (Worcestershire)
Muntin
Stay
Strut

1) Arle (Northumberland)
Arr (south and west)
Back tree (Durham)
Groin
Hang-bow
Hang-bye
Hanging style or head
Harr
Harrow (Sussex)
Hartree
Haunch
Heart tree (Norfolk)
Heel
Hingetree (Worcestershire)
Hore (Durham)
Hur (Sussex)
R-tree
Style

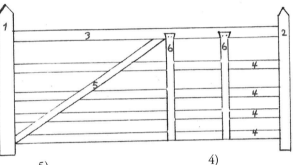

2)
Clapping style
Falling head
Flying stile
Fore tree
Shutting head
Slamming style
Striking style

5)
Brace
Dagger (North Yorkshire)
Drag-rail (Cumbria)
Lace
Sag bar (Yorkshire)
Strut
Sword (North Yorkshire)
Swording (Cumbria)

4)
Bars
Flats (Sussex)
Gate spells (Yorkshire)
Ledges (Norfolk)
Lexes (Devon)
Rails
Shivens
Shuttlebars (Devon)
Shuttles (North Devon and Somerset)
Slats
Slits

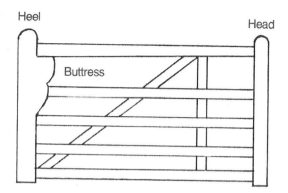

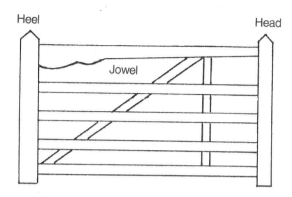

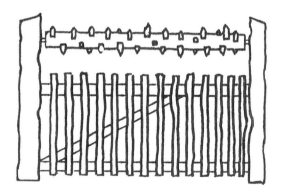

I saw this gate in an old print; it would have been made about 1800. The spiked wooden roller on the top was to deter tresspassers including mounted ones.

The sawn wood gate (normally 9' wide, sometimes 10') is basically only a frame, but because it is put on its side, it starts to sag. To counter the sag, diagonal braces are fitted, some from the top of the heel like Devon and Cornish gates and others from the bottom of the heel. The gate is only as good as the top mortice joint on the heel. This was improved upon in some areas such as Gloucestershire for instance, by incorporating a buttress under the joint and the top rail, and in other areas the top rail incorporated a jowell, which helped. In Berkshire the top rail was much thicker at the heel end than the head. Remember that the modern band hinges which hold a mortice joint together, had not at that stage been developed, and the top hinge was only a metal eye on threaded iron. Some gates like the Dorset Rod gate incorporated metal rods instead of wooden rails, but these gates were mainly used for the entrances to large estates or rectories.

One of the mistakes in making a gate, is to economise on the top rail as this increases the whip or bendiness of the whole structure.

When climbing a gate, always do so at the hanging post and not the closing head, as your weight can alter the hanging and alignment of the gate.

Details of gates and their furniture.

The different finishes to the tops of gates and gate posts.

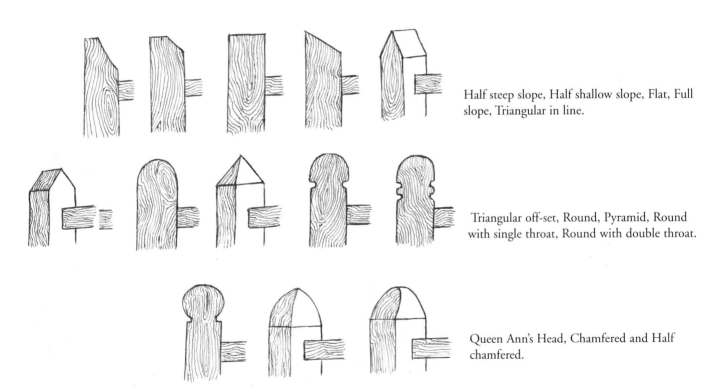

Half steep slope, Half shallow slope, Flat, Full slope, Triangular in line.

Triangular off-set, Round, Pyramid, Round with single throat, Round with double throat.

Queen Ann's Head, Chamfered and Half chamfered.

Gate Furniture.

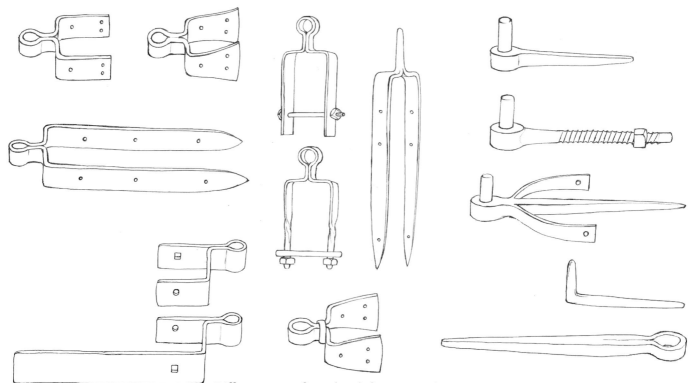

Different types of metalwork for gates and gateposts.

There are two types of gate furniture, those pieces which are attached to the gate and those that are fitted to the gate post.

On the left are hinges, bands and straps for gates, and on the right hooks for hanging gates on posts. The off centre hinges, (left middle) are for self-closing gates. Bottom right is an eye-hinge for gate hinges using bolts.

Cornish gate hinges squeeze hold of the gatepost and their position can be adjusted to line up with the hooks which are embedded in the stone post with molten lead.
The cast iron hinge on the right was probably made for a railway or canal company, and could be adjusted to suit most gate hanging positions.

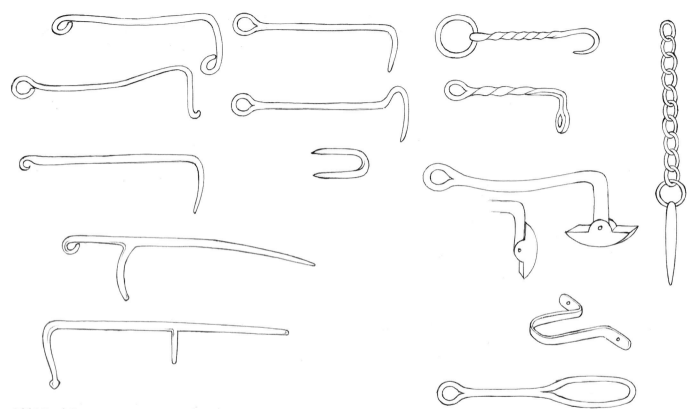

Old Metal Fasteners.

There are many different types of metal fastener and we have illustrated a few of the variations. These would all have been made by local blacksmiths, and includes hooks, sliding bolts and a clasp and eye with a metal peg on a chain. (Modern gate catches have not been included).

Three old gate catches, all hand made by local blacksmiths. Many of these catches have an "anti-chattering" device to stop cows and horses from working them open.

Some different catches.

A wooden latch, a sliding bolt and a metal catch

Some estates still have their own gates, whether by design or colour. It is nice to see gates of a certain pattern for miles on end or even painted, light blue as on one estate in Norfolk, and magenta in Northamptonshire.

It has been only the large estates, the National Trust and various authorities who have conserved the old regional and individual designs of gates, and many others are disappearing in favour of galvanised metal ones because of durability and security. As you travel round the countryside these days, you will notice that many gates are padlocked either to stop them from being stolen or to prevent entry. All too often there is a mound of earth behind the gate or an old agricultural implement; one of the drawbacks of being a landowner is the habit that some people have of dumping their household or garden rubbish in the country where it will become a danger to livestock, a health hazard and an unsightly mess.

Someone has made quite sure that nobody will be able to get into this property, but it would be a nightmare if you had to get in in a hurry!

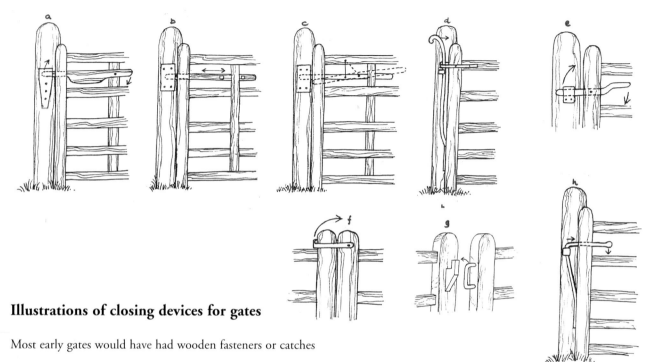

Illustrations of closing devices for gates

Most early gates would have had wooden fasteners or catches

a) This is a simple up-down latch which is weighted to hold it in the down position.
b) A sliding wooden fastener with stop pegs on the fastener.
c) A swinging latch which always stays in the closed position. All these latches are designed to deter cows and particularly horses from playing with them and opening the gates.
d) A metal spring catch for pedestrians and riders.
e) A more uncommon metal latch.
f) An up-and-over catch, mainly used where two gates close together.
g) A lift-up-and-over catch, rarely seen on wooden gates.
h) A metal spring catch, also designed to stop horses from opening it.

The bottom spur hinge is seldom used to-day and was rarely found on farm gates. It was generally used on the heavier road gates at the entrances to rectories or estates, etc. The principle of this hinge works on the thrust of the gate against the bottom of the gate post. The hinge can be adjusted to make the gate self closing or rising at the head to cope with sloping drives.

The top of a Devon gate post showing the dovetail halving joint which tightens as the brace is pulled downwards by the head of the gate.

49

The Construction of Gates

Gate heels are prepared prior to assembly. The mortices are made with chain saws and the heel is tidied up using an electric hand-planer, then the edges are chamfered and the top half chamfered.

Today the manufacture of gates is very sophisticated. The assembly takes place on a large bench about 12 feet long. The heels and heads are cut to size from sawn timber, morticed with mechanical chainsaw blades, then finished with an electric hand planer. The top rail is cut to length and the tongue or male of the mortice is cut on a band saw, then the rails and diagonals are all cut to predetermined lengths. The top and second from bottom rails which are longer are fitted first, and enough space is left to insert the other rails which are fitted into blind or half mortices: half mortice means the slot only goes halfway and not right through the head and heel; some gate makers use a full mortice on the bottom row instead of the next one up. (I'm not sure whether this is to stop the head or heel from splitting, as in the old days it was always the bottom rail which broke first, mainly from boot scraping.) Once all the rails are in position, the mortices are banged up tight, the gate is checked to make sure it is square, and is then drilled and pegged with wooden (ash) pegs, so in fact the gate is really only held together by four pegs!

Next the diagonal braces are fitted and sawn to length incorporating the correct angles. These are then fixed with bolts and screws.

The gate is turned over and the opposite braces are fitted. All the rails are bolted up with extra-long bolts where the diagonals meet on the third rail.

Because nearly all gates are made of soft wood, they are sent to be pressure treated as soon as they are assembled. The weak places on any gate are where the timber meets and creates a damp spot, and this is not helped by metal screws, although most of the metalwork on gates is galvanized today.

Modern gates are assembled in mass-production, a man finishing one in less than 30 minutes providing all the timber is correctly cut and morticed, but in the old days when oak was used a carpenter would take a whole day to complete one. Gates then were normally a fill-in job, and were mostly made in the winter.

D.I.Y gate

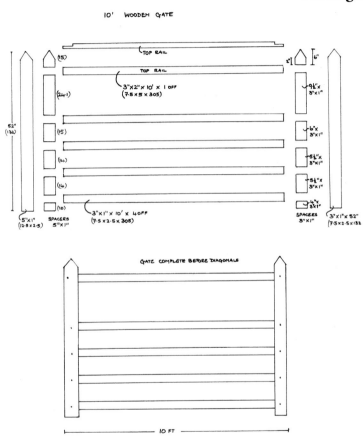

10' WOODEN GATE

TOP RAIL

TOP RAIL

3"X2" X 10' X 1 OFF
(7.5 X 5 X 305)

52"
(132)

5"X1"
(12.5 X2.5)

SPACERS
5"X1"

3"X1" X 10' X 4 OFF
(7.5 X 2.5 X 305)

2"

6"

9½"x
3"X1"

6"x
3"X1"

5½"x
3"X1"

5½"x
3"X1"

4"x
3"X1"

SPACERS
3"X1"

3"X1" X 52"
(7.5 X 2.5 X 132)

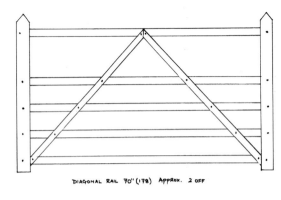

10' WOODEN GATE.

DIAGONAL RAIL 70" (178) APPROX. 2 OFF

MAKE DIAGONALS A TIGHT FIT.

GATE COMPLETE BEFORE DIAGONALS

10 FT

Diagrams not drawn to scale.

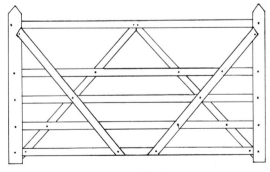

DIAGONAL RAIL 68" (173) APPROX.

IF MAKING A GATE TO FIT AN ODD SIZED OPENING
TRY TO MAKE THE DIAGONAL MEET AT THE SAME
PLACE FOR EXTRA STRENGTH.

10' Wooden Gate

There are occasions when you require a 9'6" gate or an odd size or you want to make your own to save money. If you haven't a morticing tool, and your carpentry skills are limited, this method of construction works well. I made such a gate 15 years ago and it is still going strong. The important points to remember when making gates are a) have a bold top rail, and b) brace the gate so that it will not move when it is hung except in the directions you want it to! This is why it is important to have tight square fitting joints and lots of glue, and also to ensure the timber is free of large knots and is the same size throughout.

Cut out the post pieces first, and then the cross rails. Next, cut the joints out of the top rail and start to assemble the gate. Cut out the spacers, glue and nail to the post on the floor, making sure the joints are as tight as possible. Glue the top side of the post assembly and now fix the other post board. Use oval nails to hold in place, prior to putting on the bolts and pronged nuts. You will need to counter drill the holes for the pronged nuts in order to get them to fit properly. The gate will be a bit floppy at this stage, but now add in the diagonals. You will need to chisel out the wedge pieces, or these can be precut out of the post boards to fit the diagonal rails. Put the diagonal rails in place, again with a tight fit, and nail to hold them in place while bolting up. (Use a few oval nails to do this). Drill and put a screw in the wedge cuts. Now pick up your gate. It should feel very solid and not at all bendy.

Gate irons or hinges are available at most agricultural merchants. Bolt these on, the long one on the top and the short one on the bottom. The long one must stretch along and incorporate the top rail, the bottom hinge can be moveable, so that if you are making a new gate for an old gate post, the gate can be made to fit. Creosote for extra life.

I have incorporated a step onto this gate so people can climb over it easily. This just slides on and can be screwed down.

The origin of footpaths

From earliest times animals have made tracks. We can still see these 'trods' as they are called, made by sheep where they have wandered over hills and moorland areas. Early man would have followed these tracks when hunting animals, but as he began to settle, he would have made his own tracks or footpaths to collect water, wood, minerals and stone etc, and to trade, defend and pillage. The footpaths would have been cleared of undergrowth and obstacles, with stones and wood laid across marshy areas and streams. In this way a network of paths spread, with some turning into roads.

The Romans were the great road builders in earlier times, constructing paved highways, causeways and bridges so that their armies could move around. Once off the roads, the way was narrow and often difficult, and remained that way through to the 1700s in parts of England. Celia Fiennes writing in the early eighteenth century says:

"Thence I went for Plymouth (from Chudleigh) and here the roades contract and the lanes exceeding narrow and so cover'd up you can see little about, an army might be marching undiscovered by any body, for when you are on those heights that shews a vast county about, you cannot see one road; the wayes now became so difficult that one could scarcely pass by each other, even the single, and so dirty in many places and just a track for one horses feate"

Of course other roads were wider, particularly the droving roads, but for most of the year, and particularly during winter, all these routes would have been very mucky indeed. You only have to look at a road where cattle have been moved along to realise this, and when you add in leaf mould and other vegetation, you can imagine the conditions underfoot!

This is why footpaths were so important as no vehicular or animal traffic used them, meaning that they were cleaner and often quicker for the pedestrian. Some paths were paved or cobbled in more frequented areas, but usually they were grassy tracks. In bad weather travellers would strap patens or raised wooden platforms to their feet to keep their shoes out of the puddles and mud. As people started to make enclosures or fields so stiles began to be built to improve access. Today only the main footpaths survive as many have disappeared over the centuries for a variety of reasons, but there are still thousands of tracks that are hardly used, leading through the most wonderful countryside.

The importance attached to pathways is reflected in the solid construction of stiles, particularly those in stoney country. It is interesting to note that many are constructed by gateways. Was it quicker to hop over the stile, or was the gateway muddy, or was it that the footpath users could not be trusted to close the gate? One other possibility is that, in exposed country with a stiff wind blowing, opening and closing a gate is very difficult.

Paths were most important for many reasons. Country people rarely used transport because of the cost, preferring to walk to their places of work or to buy eggs or milk and fetch water or fuel. Consequently the footpath became an important place to meet people, particularly at a gate or stile, when baskets had to be heaved over, and loads adjusted. In days gone by folk were not afraid to speak to each other, exchange the latest news, ask for directions, and of course flirt!

A troupe of Fourteenth century Mummers, who would have travelled the footpaths from village to village performing miracle plays.

The History of the word Stile

One of the biggest problems is trying to guess the age of stiles. They are not like clocks or furniture as they tended to be individually made and dating them is very difficult. Of course there are dates for various enclosures but none for the Cornish grid stiles for instance, which are in areas where there are very early enclosures. Celia Fiennes writing in the early eighteenth century says: "…..being obliged to go a mile to a parish church over some grounds which are divided by such styles and bridges uncommon and I never saw any such before; they are several stones fixed across and so are like a grate or large steps over a ditch which is full of mudd and water, and over this just in the middle a great stone fixed sideways which is the style to be clambered over."

Certainly the Celts were capable of making stiles, you only have to look at Tarr Steps on Exmoor to see this, but it was not until the Anglo-Saxons that we had written evidence of stiles in the countryside. The Anglo-Saxon word 'stig' means path or narrow way, 'stige' means going up or down, and 'stigel' means a stile or set of steps for getting over a fence.

Stile can be seen spelt in a number of ways such as stihle, steyle, steele, stiele or style, hence any place names containing or including the word could refer to a stile. There is a hamlet near Crediton called Henstill which was referred to in an early charter as Henne Stigele. Could it have been Hen's Stile? From Saxon times onwards the word stile in its various forms became very much a part of the English language, cropping up in Chaucer, Malory, Shakespeare, Trollope and Hardy.

A country woman going to market (1640). Note the pattens strapped to her shoes. These were made of wood and metal and raised the shoes out of the mud.

How a typical country lane would have looked back in the 1700's, muddy and full of pot holes, leaves and branches.

The picture on the left was taken at a Roman site in Gloucestershire and shows the adaptability of the masons of that era. (David Hasted).

The stile in the picture on the right taken at Plumpton in Yorkshire would have been quite within their capabilities. (David Hasted).

Stiles and their Classifications

There are four main categories of stile, those you walk through, those you climb over, those that are a combination of the two, and those that are loosely referred to as mechanical because they have moving parts.

Overs. In the first category some of the construction of the stiles is easy and cheap, and as a result they do not last long.

A very simple wooden stile with a double rail acting as a step. St. Gabriel, Dorset. (Roy Blake)

This is a triple double rail stile, not the easiest to climb over! High Kingston Farm, Dorchester. (Roy Blake)

An angled single step stile near Salcombe Regis.   (Roy Blake)

A straight single step stile on the Two Moors Way.   (Greg Taylor)

A right angled single step stile by a gate.   Risley, Derbyshire.   (Barbara Woodyatt)

Single abutting steps on a stile in the Kentish Weald.   (David Hasted)

A single step double stile round a gate. Pepperdon, Moretonhamstead. (Roy Blake)

This photograph of a single angled step stile was sent to me by Mary Slater. The stile is on the Offa's Dyke path and is inscribed with the verse: "There was a crooked man who walked a crooked mile, he found a crooked sixpence upon a crooked stile." There is actually a sixpence fastened to this stile!

An interesting straight single step stile set into a gate which does not open. You can see from this photograph how narrow some gateways were. Carts would not have been able to pass through this opening. Horrabridge, Devon.(Roy Blake)

A milk maid, (1805). Milk was carried from the farms and fields to the villages using a yoke across the shoulders that eased the weight of the heavy wooden buckets. The milk was sold by the measure.

Two straight steps stile beside a south Devon gate. Note how horses have been chewing the top rail of the gate. Two Moors Way. (GregTaylor)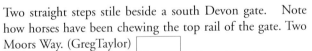

Two step stile using cut-down old telephone/electricity poles. Sheldon Centre, Bridford, Devon. (Roy Blake)

Two straight steps stile. I included this picture because of the foxgloves. They have a long flowering season in Devon, depending on how sheltered they are. The wild flowers in the hedgerows during spring and summer are incredible.   Two Moors Way. (Greg Taylor)

Two steps stile, one straight and one abutting. Two Moors Way.   (Greg Taylor)

Two straight steps stile with lifting rail for dogs. Note again the narrowness of the old gateway. Two Moors Way. (Greg Taylor) ☐
Two concrete angled steps stile, made specifically for the railways.   Two Moors Way.   (Greg Taylor) ☐

A three steps stile on the Two Moors Way.   (Greg Taylor)
Right. Three steps stile with a bar step. Porlock Coastal Path, Minehead (RoyBlake)

These are interesting stiles as they have been purpose made of reinforced concrete. Used mainly by the railways and Waterboards. Christow, Devon and Killerton, Devon. (Roy Blake)

Three angled steps aptly named The Corkscrew Stile. Newton St. Cyres, Devon. (Roy Blake)

Three stone steps for a wooden stile. Lower Dittisham, Devon. (Roy Blake)

Right. Typical Dartmoor walling incorporating a three steps stile. Hexworthy, Devon. (Roy Blake)

This is a two abutting steps stone stile, not the easiest kind to get over with those jagged coping stones. The stepping stones normally go through the wall and out the other side. Bakewell to Haddon Walk, Derbyshire. (Barbara Woodyatt)

Three abutting steps stile, solidly made in Derbyshire. Robin Hood's Inn, Baslow, Derbyshire. (David Hasted)

A Norfolk example of a three abutting steps stile. The wall is made of local stone and the steps are concrete. Walsingham, Norfolk. (David Hasted)

Three abutting steps stile in Pembroke, just by St. Non's Chapel.   (RosalindHallet)

Ladder stiles come in many designs and were mainly purchased through Estate catalogues or made locally from the 1850s onwards. This one is to be found on the Nene Way near Northampton. (Peter Spencer) ☐

This ladder stile has a stile and platform on the top. Hadrian's Wall Walk near Solway. (Mary Slater) ☐

A number of these ladder stiles were used to cross deer fencing; this elegant structure is at Horton near Paythorne, Lancashire. (David Hasted) ☐

WROUGHT-IRON WICKET GATES.

No. 101.—Made with Flat Bars to match Fences.

Height.	Width.		At Works.	Lon. or Dub.
3 ft. 6 ins.	3 ft. 6 ins.	each,	20/	21/6
3 ,, 9 ,,	3 ,, 6 ,,	,,	21/6	23/
4 ,, 0 ,,	3 ,, 6 ,,	,,	24/	25/6
Cast-iron Pillars with Bases, pair,			27/6	30/

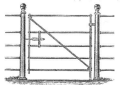

No. 101 R.—Made with Round Bars to match Fences.

Height.	Width.		At Works.	Lon. or Dub.
3 ft. 6 ins.	3 ft. 6 ins.	each,	24/	25/6
3 ,, 9 ,,	3 ,, 6 ,,	,,	25/6	27/
4 ,, 0 ,,	3 ,, 6 ,,	,,	28/6	30/
Cast-iron Pillars with Bases, pair,			27/6	30/

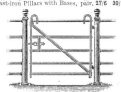

No. 102.—Made with Flat Bars to match Fences.

Height.	Width.		At Works.	Lon. or Dub.
3 ft. 6 ins.	3 ft. 6 ins.	each,	15/	16/
3 ,, 9 ,,	3 ,, 6 ,,	,,	16/	17/
Cast-iron Pillars with Bases, pair, to match Round Bar Fences			27/6	30/
If made				2/6 extra.

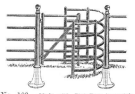

No. 103.—Made with Flat Bars to match Fences.

	At Works.	Lon. or Dub.
Wicket and Bow, 3 ft. 6 ins. high,	27/6	30/
,, 3 ,, 9 ,,	28/6	31/
Cast-iron Pillars with Bases, pair,	27/6	30/
If fitted with Movable Nose, as shown with No. 103 R, 5/ extra.		

No. 103 R.—Made with Round Bars to match Fences.

The Wicket is fitted with Movable Nose, as shown, which can be lifted up, and when turned round at right angle to Gate, allows it to open for sheep and cattle to pass through. Prices same as No. 103, with an extra 5/ for Movable Nose.

No. 104.—With Upright Bars suitable for Gardens and Pleasure Grounds.

	At Works.	Lon. or Dub.
Wicket and Bow, 3 ft. 9 ins. high,	52/6	57/6
,, 4 ,, 0 ,,	55/	60/
Cast-iron Pillars with Bases, pair,	27/6	30/
If fitted with Movable Nose, as shown with No. 103 R, 5/ extra.		

BIPED-PASS AND FOOTPATH POSTS.

BIPED PASS.

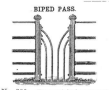

FOOTPATH POSTS.

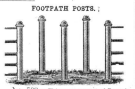

No. 390.—The special advantage of this Pass is that people can walk through at pleasure, but horses, cattle, and sheep cannot get through.

PRICES.	At Works.	Lon. or Dub.
For Fences 3 ft. 6 ins. to 4 ft. high, ... each,	12/6	14/
Cast-iron Terminals, with Bases, ... per pair,	27/6	30/

No. 702.—This arrangement of Posts is a simple means of making a road for foot passengers through bar or other Fencing, whilst excluding horses and carriages.

PRICES.	At Works.	Lon. or Dub.
Post 3 ft. 6 ins. high, with Flanges for Stone, ... each,	12/	13/6
Post 3 ft. 6 ins. high, with Self-fixing Bases, ... each,	16/	18/

IRON FENCE STEPS.

They allow persons to get over the Fences easily, without injuring the Bars or Wires. We submit here two descriptions.

PRICES.		At Works.	Lon. or Dub.
No. 65,	... each,	30/	32/6
,, 391,	... ,,	15/	16/6

No. 65.

No. 391.

WROUGHT-IRON HALF-BOW, FOR GATES AND WICKETS.

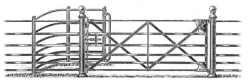

Half-Bow No. 718 is specially adapted for fixing on the one side of a Fence only, in connection with Bar and Wire Fences, and any of the Gates on pages 16 to 17, and Wickets on foregoing page, can be supplied with this Bow.

		At Works.	Lon. or Dub.
Half-Bow, fitted with Movable Nose, ... each,		17/6	19/

For Prices of Gates, Wickets, and Pillars, see pages 14 to 21.

GLASGOW, LONDON, DUBLIN, EDINBURGH, AND CALCUTTA.

A page from a Victorian catalogue

A Victorian iron ladder stile at Bigham Hall near Durwath, Cumbria. (David Hasted)

A wooden apex ladder straddling a stone wall. Just as well the ladder is there as I feel the wall would probably fall down if touched! Walla Crag, near Ashness Bridge, Cumbria. (Barbara Woodyatt)

A simple beaters' ladder stile attached to a straining post. Antony House, near Plymouth, Devon. (M.D.L.R.)

A stout ladder stile, well used. Sour Milk Gill, Seathwaite, the Lake District. (Nyree Fearnley)

A small ladder stile and platform over a Devon wall next to a classic south Devon gate. The Two Moors Way.   (Greg Taylor)

A shepherd carrying a crook and lamb (1642). Shepherds could walk miles in a day looking after their sheep. Their way to work would have been along a network of footpaths.

Staircase stiles come in a wide variety of designs. This one is built beside a gate. Dale Dyke Reservoir, Bradfield Dale, Sheffield. (David Hasted)

One way of creating access to some fishing over a high wall of faced stone: a stout wooden stairway near Ogden, Oldham, Lancashire. (David Hasted)

A wooden stairway over a Devon bank on the Two Moors Way. (Greg Taylor)

One way to cross a Cornish bank: wooden stairs on the South Coastal Path, Boswinger, Cornwall. (Roy Blake)

A very accessible wooden stair stile at Cat Crags, River Wharfe, Yorkshire. (David Hasted)

A Cornish granite stair stile set in the corner of two walls at Langewednack on the Lizard Peninsula, Cornwall. (Roy Blake)

Right. Metal steps in a stone wall. Aveton Gifford, Devon. (M.D.L.R.)

These Cornish grid stiles, forerunners of the metal cattle grids of today, are very old but no one seems to know when they were built. This ancient one is in the churchyard at St. Levens, a magical place not far from Land's End. You can see the central plinth for the body to be rested on and there are seats either side for the coffin bearers. (M.D.L.R.)

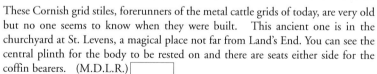

A Cornish grid stile on the 'Coffin Way' near Zennor, Cornwall. (David Hasted) These lych paths were closely followed when carrying the dead to the church, and the funeral procession did not deviate because wherever a dead body was carried a new public right of way would be created. The corpse would have been carried on a hurdle or planks of wood as coffins were rare before the nineteenth century.

A distant view of the ancient Celtic fields near Zennor, Cornwall, with a typical stile, grid and granite bar across, in the foreground. (David Hasted)

This is an unusual Cornish grid stile which rises and bends round. Note the wild plants. Erisey Barton, Lizard Peninsular, Cornwall. (Margaret Bailey)

Two slightly different Cornish grid / step stiles on the walk from Zennor to St. Ives, Cornwall. (David Hasted)

Here are some extracts taken from William Hone's The Every-Day Book 1827 which give an insight to footpaths at that time:

"I love our real old English footpaths. I love those rustic and picturesque stiles, opening their pleasant escapes from frequented places, and dusty highways, into the solitudes of nature. It is delightful to catch a glimpse of one on the village green, under the old elder-tree by some ancient cottage, or half hidden by the overhanging boughs of a wood. I love to see the smooth dry track, winding away in easy curves, along some green slope, to the churchyard, to the embosomed cottage, or to the forest grange."

"What is there so truly English? What is so linked with our rural tastes, our sweetest memories, and our sweetest poetry, as stiles and field paths? Goldsmith, Thomson, and Milton have adorned them with some of their richest wreaths. They have consecrated them to poetry and love. It is along the footpath in secluded fields, - upon the stile in the embowered lane, - where the wild-rose and the honey-suckle are lavishing their beauty and their fragrance, that we delight to picture to ourselves rural lovers, breathing in the dewy sweetness of a summer evening vows still sweeter."

"Again I say, I love fieldpaths, and stiles of all species, - ay, even the most inaccessible piece of rustic erection ever set up in defiance of age, laziness, and obesity. How many scenes of frolic and merry confusion have I seen at a clumsy stile! What exclamations, and charming blushes, and fine eventual vaulting on the part of the ladies, and what an opportunity does it afford to beaux of exhibiting a variety of gallant and delicate attentions. I consider a rude stile as any thing but an impediment in the course of a rural courtship."

"Those good old turn-stiles too, - can I ever forget them? The hours I have spun round upon them, when a boy; or those in which I have almost laughed myself to death at the remembrance of my village pedagogue's disaster! Me-thinks I see him now. The time a sultry day; - the domine a goodly person of some eighteen or twenty stone; - the scene a footpath sentinelled with turn-stiles, one of which held him fast, as in utter amazement at his bulk. Never shall I forget his efforts and agonies to extricate himself, nor his lion-like roars, which brought some labourers to his assistance, who, when they had recovered from their convulsions of laughter, knocked off the top, and let him go. It is long since I saw a turnstile, and I suspect the Falstaffs have cried them down. But, without a jest, stiles and fieldpaths are vanishing everywhere."

A pastry seller (1689) on his way to the next hamlet with warm pies and tarts for sale.

This metal stile seems to have a kind of grid to step on which would allow the mud to fall through and stop it from becoming too slippery! Maeshafn, Denbighshire. (Hazel Massey)

A baker's delivery man (1805). He would have been seen on footpaths near towns and villages, on his way to sell bread to outlying cottages and farms.

This metal stile, potentially lethal for the shins, is to be found near Topsham, Devon. (Roy Blake)

Left. Metal stiles come in a range of sizes and shapes. Here is an old one (left) on the Bakewell to Haddon walk, Derbyshire. (Barbara Woodyatt)

I was particularly pleased to receive this photograph of a toe-hole slab stile. It must be quite difficult to get over but there is a step on the side of the slab to help.   Aveton Gifford, South Devon. (Roy Blake)

A simple slab stile no more than three foot high down some steps. Crudwell, Wiltshire.   (David Hasted)

A slab stile beautifully made in the early 1800s. The slab drops into a grooved pillar either side. Catbrook near Tintern, Monmouthshire. (Rosalind Hallett)

A chimney sweep (1884). He would have had a round of villages to call at and would have walked to them all. Incidentally the soot was put on the gardens to prevent slugs from eating the vegetables.

Not often seen, a rod or bar stile set into a wall at Rodney Stoke near Cheddar, Somerset. (Roy Blake)

Throughs. The second main category of stiles.

These are found mainly in the North. This stile has straight side walls which must have been quite difficult for women or overweight men to pass through in olden times. There are flat stones either side so that any load such as a basket or sack could be rested on the top while the bearer negotiated the gap. Stiles were great meeting places in the old days, and one can imagine people stopping to gossip and exchange news as they rested their bundles on the stone slabs before continuing on their way. Nowadays rucksacks have replaced the bundles and baskets that people used to carry, but the flat slabs still come in very useful for people who want to stop for a breather. The gate is to stop young lambs from trespassing. Bear Park, Carperby, North Yorkshire. (David Hasted)

Here there is a little more ankle room although the walls have been fitted with narrowers to prevent livestock from getting through. Gayle church in the background near Hawes, North Yorkshire. (David Hasted)

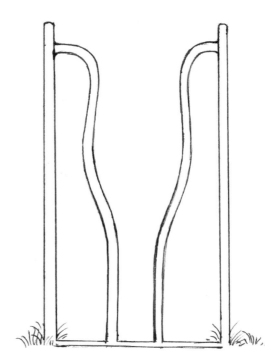

This is a drawing of a metal squeezer typical of those found around the Bath area. It is called The Fat Man's Agony, and indeed, many a corpulence must have become wedged between the bars over the years! Perhaps we should have this sort of stile at the entrances to fast food shops!

Left. A metal squeezer stile made of iron pipe for the local Water Board. Monkton Combe near Bath. (M.D.L.R.)

This wedge stile is to be found near Glastonbury Tor in Somerset.   (M.D.L.R.)

Right. A wooden vee stile leading into the churchyard at Laycock, Wiltshire.   If you have never been to Laycock, you should try to go as it is quite fascinating. It is situated just south of Chippenham, Wiltshire.   (M.D.L.R.)

You can see the work that has gone into making the two pillars for this squeezer stile near Callow and Kirk, Ireton in Derbyshire. (David Hasted)

Left, A beautiful wedge or squeezer with an iron livestock bar. There are several of these at Farrington Gurney in Somerset. (M.D.L.R)

Here is a wedge stile made from a huge slab of stone at Chiselborough near Yeovil, Somerset. (Roy Blake)

Right. A squeezer on Heptonstall Moor near Hurstwood, Lancashire. (David Hasted)

A modern squeezer cut into a metal gate near Brean Down, Cornwall. (Roy Blake)

Left. A modern concrete squeezer at Clyst St. George near the estuary of the river Exe, Devon. (Roy Blake)

Another variation of a vee stile is an off-set wedge. This one is at Willfoot Farm, Twiston, Lancashire. (David Hasted)

This is a Lancashire squeezer which leaves just enough room for the ankles and calves. Holme, near Holmfirth. (David Hasted)

Zigzag stiles come in various different designs, allowing the user to squeeze round but preventing livestock from turning once they are in the 'v'. This one is at Bogside near Larkhall, Lanarkshire. (David Hasted)

Another zigzag stile on Ranmoor Common near Dorking, Surrey. (David Hasted)

This is a stone zigzag which leaves just enough room for the feet to be shuffled round. Near Holmfirth, West Yorkshire. (David Hasted) ☐

This post type stile is made up of three stone pillars which are off-set to allow the passage of humans but not animals. A similar system is to be found in Spanish bull fighting rings, to allow the matador and his troup to gain the safety of the barricades. North Rigton, York. (David Hasted) ☐

Combinations (Overs). The third main category of stiles.

This Cornish stile combines a slab and a step to climb over it. Carn Towan near Sennen, Cornwall. (M.D.L.R.) ☐

Right. This slab stile has a step up to it and a lamb gate the other side. Flockton Moor, West Yorkshire. (David Hasted) ☐

Two slightly different slab stiles. The one on the left is at Catbrook near Tintern, Monmouthshire, (Rosalind Hallett), and the one on the right is at Elkstone near Cirencester, Gloucestershire. (M.D.L.R.)

This is a rather sad two step stile which used to look like the illustration on the right but is now reduced to half its size by wear and tear and weather. It is reputed to be very old, but was first mentioned as recently as 1860, and the way it has deteriorated over the last few decades makes this most unlikely as it is made of very soft sandstone. It is a pity that the local people have not restored this landmark to its former glory. Froyle (on the A31 in a layby past the Hen and Chickens Inn), Hampshire. (M.D.L.R.)

A Welsh two steps and bar stile. I am not sure what the hole was used for but certainly dogs would love it. Maeshafn, Denbighshire, North Wales. (Hazel Massey) ☐

Right. A well used two steps and raised slab at Deers' Leap, Priddy, near Wells in Somerset. (M.D.L.R) ☐

A Pinder, (Saxon). He was a kind of 'animal warden' who collected up any stray animals and put them in the local pound. In the days of open farming and few enclosures, he was probably kept quite busy!

Another Welsh stile with two abutting steps and a raised slab. Again in North Wales at Trelawned, Denbighshire. (Hazel Massey)

Three steps and a raised slab with a hole cut through it for the local cat or small dog. Bantham Village near Kingsbridge, Devon. (Roy Blake) ☐

Left. Three steps and raised slab stile. Notice how worn the steps are, and imagine how much use they had in the old days! Plumpton, Yorkshire. (David Hasted) ☐

The next three pictures are interesting slab stairs and step stiles which were expertly made by prisoners on the Beaufort Estate awaiting transportation to Australia at the beginning of the nineteenth century. These prisoners were housed at Botany Bay Camp which was named after their destination in Australia.   Catbrook near Tintern, Monmouth. (Rosalind Hallett)

Catbrook near Tintern, Monmouth. (Rosalind Hallett). ☐

A similar type of stile but further round the coast at Llantwit Major near Bridgend, Glamorgan. (David Hasted) ☐

Two coffin stiles, slab and step and slab and stairs near the church at Llanfrynach, Cowbridge in South Glamorgan. (Ron Norton)

A two abutting steps stile in a stone wall in North Wales, Trelawned, Denbighsire. (Hazel Massey).

Right. Raised slab and abutting steps at the Farm at the Beamish Museum, Tyne and Wear. (M.D.L.R.)

An amazing stone stile. A huge amount of work must have gone into constructing these great granite pillars and the mortices to hold the granite cross beams. Killerton Estate, N.T. north of Exeter, Devon. (Roy Blake).

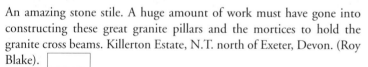

Right. The contrasting simplicity of this rough slate stile works well as a livestock and human barrier. Near Padstow, Cornwall. (Roy Blake).

This two slab and one step stile made of faced slate is to be found near Padstow in Cornwall. (Roy Blake)

Left. This two step bar stile was also made by the prisoners on the Beaufort Estate who were awaiting transportation. Catbrook near Tintern, Monmouthshire. (Rosalind Hallett)

Here is a step-in and step-out variety of corner stile on the Dalesway in Yorkshire. (Dorothy Kyne)

Another corner stile which I have included because it looks rather difficult to get over. Ottery St. Mary, Devon. (Roy Blake)

Combinations (throughs).

This is a step-over vee or squeezer stile which has been recently restored. The path leads to the beautiful Norman church at Combes near Brighton in Sussex. (M.D.L.R.)

Left. This is a vee stile with a lamb guard.   You have to walk round the 'L' shaped slabs and then go through the vee.   Lower Bracken Hill Farm, Silsden, Yorkshire. (David Hasted)

Two stepped vee or squeezer stiles, different in construction but made to last. Left hand side: Old Town near Hebden Bridge, Yorkshire, (David Hasted), and right hand side: the Bakewell to Hadden Walk, Derbyshire. (Barbara Woodyatt)

A straight squeezer with step, solidly made on Dartmoor near Yelverton, Devon. (Mary Bailey)

A Hayward, (Saxon). He was responsible for all the fences and ditches in the area, and also supervised the early sowings of oats, barley, peas, beans and vetches.

Above. A modern wooden step-up vee stile at Dorsington near Stratford upon Avon, Warwickshire. (M.D.L.R.)

Right. A wooden straight squeezer stile with a step. Halford south of Bovey Tracey, Devon.   (Roy Blake)

A one step vee squeezer stile with a slab behind on the coastal path near Lannacombe Beach, South Devon. (Roy Blake)

An Exmoor vee squeezer. I believe this kind is meant to be deer proof. Near Bulland Lodge, Wiveliscombe, Somerset. (M.D.L.R.)

117

Step-over squeezers. This double stile was designed to allow a coffin to pass over the top.   It is not known whether the two iron bars were put across to strengthen the slabs or to deter cyclists.   Horton in Ribblesdale, North Yorkshire. (David Hasted) ☐

Here is the same feature on a step-over stile at Glastonbury Tor, Somerset. (David Hasted) ☐

A carpenter (1867). He would have travelled from farm to farm wearing his traditional paper hat and with his canvas bag of tools slung over his shoulder.

A two step straight squeezer stile in Walden Dale, Yorkshire. (David Hasted)

119

A step-over straight squeezer stile with abutting steps at Cockwill Hill, Silsden, Yorkshire. (David Hasted)

A step-over squeezer with abutting steps and a lamb gate. Aincliffe, Yorkshire Dales. (Margaret Bailey)

A straight squeezer with abutting steps and stairs at Oaklands Farm, Higher Barronford, Lancashire. (David Hasted)

A wedge with stairs and a lamb gate near Winskill, Cumbria. (David Hasted)

A bastard stile, so called because it is neither a true gate nor a true stile but a combination of the two. Winterbourne Zelston, Dorset. (M.D.L.R.)

A gate within a gate made specially for walkers, near Sherrel Farm, Ivybridge, Devon. (Roy Blake)

Mechanical.

The next section of stiles can be loosely called Mechanical as they involve a moving part or parts.

Two sliding rail stiles, the left one from Sidbury, Devon, (Roy Blake), and the right one from Selbourne in Hampshire. (David Hasted)

A lift-up gate stile in the village of Dinder near Wells, Somerset. (M.D.L.R.)

A top-opening wedge stile. The top lifts up to allow the walker through but there is a central hanging bar to prevent sheep and lambs from getting out. This is near the farm at Pickedstones on Exmoor, Devon. (Roy Blake)

These photographs show a wedge stile with a moving top rail. This stile used to be at Abinger Roughs, (N.T.) in Surrey, but has been replaced by a gate. (Mr. D.G.Cornford)

A lift-up and walk-through wooden stile at Poltesco on the Lizard Peninsula, Cornwall.   (Roy Blake)

A walk-through scissors stile leading to the old Saxon church at Duntisbourne Rouse near Cirencester, Gloucestershire. (M.D.L.R.)

This mechanical stile was invented by Thomas Lyne who lived in Malmesbury and was a milliner and draper. He later became an inventor and created a folding harrow and this stile which is opened by lifting the knob on top of the moving post. The posts fall open to allow passage and click back afterwards; there is a geared mechanism at ground level. This stile leads into the churchyard at Ashton Keynes in Wiltshire. There is also another example in the churchyard at Mells in Somerset. (Left: Roy Blake, right: David Hasted)

Here are three different mechanical stiles. The first two exist but I have been unable to find an example of the one on the right. Perhaps someone will find one for me!

Left. This is a very beautiful wrought iron opening stile, with a raised round step either side. The central bottle shaped parts move outwards to allow passage through. This stile is to be found in a private garden near Tonbridge Wells

Centre. A mechanical stile opening with a top lever on one of the falling posts. This is very similar to the Thomas Lyne invention.

Right. I found this design in an old book. It is a similar system to that of the previous stile, but alas, no one knows where to find one so far. A knob on one of the falling posts is pulled up to open the stile, which was manufactured by Messrs F. Morton & Co.

Top. A nice example of a kissing gate at Stanton near Winchcombe in Gloucestershire. Note the beautiful swan's head and neck on the hinge post. (M.D.L.R.)

Here is a modern wooden kissing gate with a closing catch. Walkers Hill, Wiltshire. (Chris Cole)

A modern galvanised kissing gate in North Meadow, Cricklade, Gloucestershire. This watery scene is a powerful reminder of the floods that inundated much of the country during the winter of 2000/2001. (Chris Cole)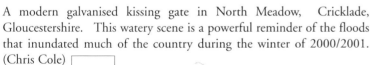

A metal kissing gate set in a wall near St. Donats, Glamorganshire, Wales. (David Hasted)

This kissing gate has a ball and chain to keep it closed as there is a rather large passing place where animals could get round if it were left open. Compton Greenfield near Bristol. (M.D.L.R.)

Left. A kissing gate leading into a churchyard at Luckington, Wiltshire. (Chris Cole)

These stiles are variously known as clapper or ladies' stiles, or falling and tumbling stiles. There are more around England than one is led to believe, many of them copies. I am not sure which is the oldest, possibly the one at Linton, Cambridgeshire, although the Charlecote clapper in Warwickshire has a long history.

The clapper stile at Charlecote near Stratford upon Avon, Warwickshire. This has been restored and iron bands have been fitted to the heads of the clappers. (M.D.L.R.)

Probably the oldest in England, this clapper stile is at Linton, Cambridgeshire. (David Hasted)

134

There are two clapper stiles in the churchyard at Chedzoy, (known locally as Chidgey) in Somerset, and others to be found at Sissinghurst Castle, Kent and Benthall Hall, (N.T.) at Broseley near Ironbridge in Shropshire. (M.D.L.R.)

Turnstile gates were more fun for country children than kissing gates as turnstiles revolved. You can imagine the kind of games that must have been played on them, and the cuts and bruises that probably resulted!

This pair of turnstiles is on the holy island of Lindisfarne, Northumberland. It is possible that they were made locally in the shape of ox yokes from a wooden or stone pattern. (David Hasted)

Left. This simple turnstile is set in the grounds of Waverley Abbey near Farnham in Surrey. (Catherine Aneja)

Left. A turnstile at East Knoyle in Wiltshire. Although this stile has stood here for more than two hundred years, in recent times there have been requests to move it, once from a portly vicar and secondly from wheel-chair users. It has now been adapted so that it can be removed if necessary! (Robin Hammond)

Middle. Here is a turnstile in a pathway at Ottery St. Mary, Devon.(Roy Blake)

Right. Another turnstile, recently restored at Wicklewood near Wymondham in Norfolk. (David Hasted)

Centre revolving gates or Tapsel gates.
It is hard to know whether to class these as gates or stiles or both, as certainly some have provision for people to climb over. I have classed them as both.

Top. This Tapsel gate has a kind of stile incorporated in the middle. East Dean near Beachy Head in Sussex. (David Hasted)

Left. This attractive Tapsel gate is at Jevington in Sussex. (David Hasted)

This is an ingenious gate with a stile built into it in the churchyard at Compton Greenfield near Bristol.   (M.D.L.R.)

139

This is a fascinating stile not far from Belstone near Okehampton in Devon. The farmer has used the original holes for a pole gate thus also creating a stile that can be dismantled, and is probably no more than 5 foot wide. (Roy Blake)

This is one of the British Fence and Gate Company's Rambler Stiles incorporating hinge-back posts and chains. They are mainly found in the south of England. Uplowman near Tiverton, Devon. (Roy Blake)

Oddities.

Originally this was just a squeezer stile then bars and a step were added later. Judging by the state of the ground, most people use the wicket gate. Tan Hill Way, Wiltshire. (Chris Cole)

There was an old stone stile here but it was obviously in the way of the drive so a new wooden stile was put up next to it. Dovedale, Derbyshire. (Chris Cole)

These two rams with pillars make a very flamboyant stile. The more the merrier; well done that landowner! Holwich Scar, Teesdale. (David Hasted)

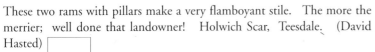

What a contrast! A tractor tyre filled with rubble makes a rough and ready stile. West Knighton, Dorset. (David Hasted)

These 'wellie gates' had to be included, and in fact the soles of these rubber boots make very good self-closing hinges! Left hand side: the pathway from Muker to Thwaite, (Mary Slater), and right hand side: Dentdale, Cumbria. (David Hasted)

These are both rather sad stiles. The hedges either side have been removed to make the fields more economic to use, leaving the stiles marooned as reminders of former times. Left hand side: Lyn Hill, Shropshire. (DavidJones) Right hand side: Monmouth, Wales. (John A. Hudson)

Time to be replaced. This stile has been cobbled together and must be nearly impossible to get over. There is no room to swing your leg over and the gate is locked! Risely, Derbyshire / Nottinghamshire border. (Barbara Woodyatt)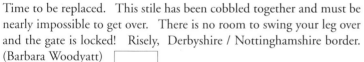

An overgrown stile. I don't think this happens so much these days, but certainly until about ten years ago the intrepid walker was quite often faced with situations like this. (Roy Blake)

and finally . . .

I love this photograph. 'Right, who's dares come first?' rather sums it up at this bridge stile to be found at Bishops Cannings in Wiltshire. (Chris Cole)

Country Codes

Close all gates unless you find them open.

Do not leave any litter; take it home with you. Crisp packets, chocolate wrappers, fizzy drink cans and plastic bottles seem to be the usual eye-sores: they do not bio-degrade, and last forever.

Food that is not eaten should be wrapped up carefully and taken home. Don't throw it away.

Fire can be a very serious problem and can easily be started by a cigarette end, particularly during dry spells. Beware of the possible consequences of your actions.

Dogs must be on leads at all times unless you have permission to let them off from the farmer. It is not only sheep that can be disturbed by dogs, but also nesting and brooding birds.

Do not pick wild flowers or dig up wild plants such as bluebells, cowslips or daffodils. Leave them for others to enjoy and besides, they are protected by law.

Leave scissors and secateurs at home. Taking holly, ivy etc is stealing.

Don't take any shortcuts, keep to the recognised path. You might think you are saving time but it could lead to a stone wall collapsing under you or a nasty gash from barbed wire or a rusty nail.

If you see a sheep on its back, roll it over onto its legs. They can be very heavy if wet. Sometimes the sheep can be a bit dazed, but at least you will have saved its eyes from the crows. Of course it will not realise this and will usually run off without so much as a thank you! Be aware of the fact that sheep might be sleeping or even sunbathing; they often look quite dead until you approach them.

Ricketty gates.   Some farmers aren't very worried about the state of their gates and whether or not they swing open, or the fact that they are often tied up with string.   Climb over with care at the hinge end of the gate.   Don't try to undo the string if there is any as the whole gate might collapse!

Beware of walking with your dogs through cattle, particularly on sloping ground. Heifers, cows and bullocks are very curious about dogs and will come bounding over to investigate, sometimes forgetting to brake.   If this happens take off your coat, swing it round and flap it vigorously, then pick up your dog if it's small enough or let it off the lead and head for the nearest gate or stile.

If there is a problem with access such as a broken gate or stile, write to the local Parish Council.   This will normally be handled at a local level rather than involving other organisations or councils.   For information about this try the nearest shop or pub.

Last of all, you are a guest in the countryside, you don't own it and therefore please respect it at all times and leave it as you found it. Remember, farmers and landowners are only stewards of the land and there are the odd bad eggs just as there are walkers who complain about everything!   The important thing is - enjoy yourself!

Some of the Stiles constructed by the author

The supply and erection of
fencing, gates, agricultural and leisure based products.
The application of traditional country skills for
logging, hedge layering, drystone walling and coppicing.

Winterborne Zelston Fencing
Winterborne Zelston
Blandford Forum
Dorset DT11 9EU
Telephone 01929 459245
Facsimile 01929 459011
Mobile 0831-10-16-71

Proprietor: Major J. R. I. Bower

VAT No. 355 7007 56

PENNYMOOR TIMBER

Pennymoor Timber, Pennymoor, Tiverton, Devon. EX16 8LJ
Telephone: (01363) 866262   Fax: (01363) 866840

GOLD COCKEREL BOOKS

For further information about our series of books

please visit our Website at:

www.goldcockerelbooks.co.uk

or write to us at:

**Gold Cockerel Books, Kennerleigh
Nr. Crediton, Devon, EX17 4RS**